THIS COLORING BOOK BELONGS TO:

Emma

This page is intentionally left blank to keep the ink from bleeding through to the next coloring page.

This page is intentionally left blank to keep the ink from bleeding through to the next coloring page.

MADRIGUERA

*This page is intentionally left blank to keep the ink
from bleeding through to the next coloring page.*

MADRIGUERA

*This page is intentionally left blank to keep the ink
from bleeding through to the next coloring page.*

MADRIGUERA

This page is intentionally left blank to keep the ink from bleeding through to the next coloring page.

MADRIGUERA

This page is intentionally left blank to keep the ink
from bleeding through to the next coloring page.

This page is intentionally left blank to keep the ink from bleeding through to the next coloring page.

*This page is intentionally left blank to keep the ink
from bleeding through to the next coloring page.*

MADRIGUERA

*This page is intentionally left blank to keep the ink
from bleeding through to the next coloring page.*

MADRIGUERA

*This page is intentionally left blank to keep the ink
from bleeding through to the next coloring page.*

MADRIGUERA

This page is intentionally left blank to keep the ink from bleeding through to the next coloring page.

MADRIGUERA

This page is intentionally left blank to keep the ink from bleeding through to the next coloring page.

MADRIGUERA

This page is intentionally left blank to keep the ink from bleeding through to the next coloring page.

MADRIGUERA

This page is intentionally left blank to keep the ink from bleeding through to the next coloring page.

MADRIGUERA

This page is intentionally left blank to keep the ink from bleeding through to the next coloring page.

*This page is intentionally left blank to keep the ink
from bleeding through to the next coloring page.*

This page is intentionally left blank to keep the ink from bleeding through to the next coloring page.

MADRIGUERA

*This page is intentionally left blank to keep the ink
from bleeding through to the next coloring page.*

MADRIGUERA

*This page is intentionally left blank to keep the ink
from bleeding through to the next coloring page.*

MADRIGUERA

*This page is intentionally left blank to keep the ink
from bleeding through to the next coloring page.*

MADRIGUERA

This page is intentionally left blank to keep the ink from bleeding through to the next coloring page.

MADRIGUERA

*This page is intentionally left blank to keep the ink
from bleeding through to the next coloring page.*

MADRIGUERA

This page is intentionally left blank to keep the ink from bleeding through to the next coloring page.

MADRIGUERA
Copyrighted Material

Made in the USA
Monee, IL
30 May 2022

97230421R00031